EGMONT

We bring stories to life

First published in Great Britain 2009
by Egmont UK Limited
239 Kensington High Street
London W8 6SA

Originally published in Indonesia in 2008 by Komik Warna.

Ben 10 and all related characters and elements
are trademarks of and © Cartoon Network.
(s09)

ISBN 978 1 4052 4804 4
1 3 5 7 9 10 8 6 4 2

Printed in Italy

CREATED BY
DUNCAN ROULEAU, JOE CASEY,
JOE KELLY AND STEVEN T. SEAGLE

WILDMUTT

GHOSTFREAK

HEATBLAST

BEN
TENNYSON

DIAMONDHEAD

VOLUME 3
THE KRAKKEN

WRITTEN BY
MAN OF ACTION

A *FULL MOON SHINES* OUT OVER A LAKE IN THE COUNTRYSIDE.

BEN TENNYSON IS LOOKING FOR SOME FUN.

CANNON BALL!

SPLASH!

THE JUDGES GIVE HIM A PERFECT TEN! YEAH! THE CROWD LOVE HIM!

A PERFECT DWEEB IS MORE LIKE IT.

COME ON! DIVE IN!

ARE YOU KIDDING? WHO KNOWS WHAT KIND OF NASTY THINGS ARE SWIMMING AROUND IN THERE.

YOU ARE SO BUSTED WHEN I TELL GRANDPA!

HMMPH!

I CAN'T BELIEVE SHE FELL FOR IT! A MONSTER IN THE LAKE . . . HOW STUPID CAN SHE BE?

THEN SUDDENLY, A DARK SHAPE RISES OUT OF THE WATER.

SPLASH!

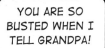

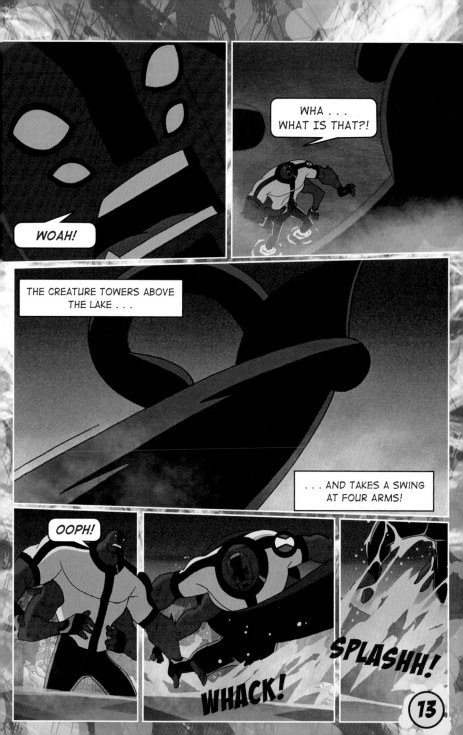

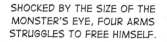

SHOCKED BY THE SIZE OF THE MONSTER'S EYE, FOUR ARMS STRUGGLES TO FREE HIMSELF.

GULP!

AAAGH!

ERGH!

HAAAA!

SPLASH!

15

I'M MAX TENNYSON AND THIS IS MY GRANDSON, BEN. WE CHARTERED YOUR BOAT TODAY FOR A FISHING TRIP.

WHAT ARE YOU WAITING FOR THEN? A FANCY INVITATION? GET ABOARD, I HAVEN'T GOT ALL DAY.

COOL . . .

THEY SET OUT TOWARDS THE MIDDLE OF THE LAKE.

ANYTHING INTERESTING TO CATCH OUT THERE TODAY?

MORE THAN YOU CAN IMAGINE. LOOKS LIKE YOUR BOY IS USING HIS BREAKFAST AS BAIT.

25

GLOOP!

HEY! YOU DID THAT ON PURPOSE!

WHOOSH!

THIS IS THE END!

GULP!

XLR8 CARRIES THE OTHER PEOPLE TO SAFETY ON THE SHORE.

HUH?

WHAT HAPPENED?

THE KRAKKEN RIPS OPEN THE CRATES ON THE DECK WITH ITS SHARP, VICIOUS TEETH!

NOOO!

YOU CAN'T STEAL THIS ONE! NO! NEVER!

FWOOSH!

XLR8 GRABS HOLD OF THE KRAKKEN'S TENTACLE.

THEN HE RUNS WITH ALL HIS MIGHT, PULLING THE KRAKKEN'S TENTACLE AWAY FROM THE CRATES.

SWOOSH!

JONAH IS KNOCKED TO THE FLOOR.

THWACK!

THUD!

OWW!

ROAARRR!

GRRR!

ROARING WITH PAIN, THE KRAKKEN DIVES BACK INTO THE WATER.

SPLASH!

THANKS FOR THE HAND. AND FOR THE FEET!

WHAT'S SO IMPORTANT IN THAT CRATE THAT YOU'D RISK YOUR *OWN LIFE* FOR IT?

UM . . . OUR LUNCH.

THWACK!

YOU RISKED GETTING EATEN FOR A FEW SANDWICHES?

CANNERY

FWOOSH!

BUT THE KRAKKEN REFUSES TO GIVE UP! IT GRABS HOLD OF THE CRATES AND PULLS THEM UNDER THE WATER.

SPLASSSH!

THE OMNITRIX BEGINS TO BEEP.

UH, OOPS. SORRY, GOTTA RUN!

F.O.F

BUT BEN IS TOO SLOW.

EEUGH!

HE TURNS BACK INTO HIS HUMAN FORM WHILST STILL IN THE MIDDLE OF THE LAKE!

GRANDPA!

SHAW, BEN IS OVERBOARD! BRING THE BOAT AROUND.

HUH?

NEXT TIME YOU'RE IN MY SIGHTS, YOU WON'T BE SO LUCKY.

SEE, I TOLD YOU! THAT WAS THE THING THAT ATTACKED ME LAST NIGHT.

CAPTAIN SHAW WAS RIGHT!

JUST BECAUSE HE WAS RIGHT ABOUT THE KRAKKEN, IT DOESN'T MEAN THAT I WAS WRONG ABOUT HIM. I WANT YOU TO STAY AWAY FROM THAT GUY. HE'S TROUBLE!

HMPH. YOU'RE JUST BEING STUBBORN.

YEAH, DON'T YOU JUST HATE PEOPLE LIKE THAT?

WE'LL LEAVE THIS TO THE EXPERTS, BEN. LIKE THOSE 'FRIENDS OF FISH' GUYS.

46

I'M AFRAID THIS IS JUST GOING TO HAVE TO BE THE ONE THAT GOT AWAY, BEN.

...RTS? WHO ...ER TO SNAG A ...E MONSTER TH... A GUY WITH A MO...STER-BUSTER ON HIS WRIST?

CAPTAIN SHAW, WHAT IS IT?

HERE'S THE LOW DOWN, THOSE MEN ARE NO FISH KISSERS.

THE NERVE OF THOSE ENVIRO-PUNKS. THEY SHUT DOWN THE ENTIRE LAKE! NOBODY TELLS ME WHERE TO SAIL!

AND NOBODY'S GONNA KEEP ME AWAY FROM REELING IN THE CATCH OF THE CENTURY. NOBODY!

CAPTAIN SHAW DIVES TO THE BOTTOM OF THE LAKE, SEARCHING FOR SIGNS OF THE KRAKKEN . . .

HE NOTICES SOMETHING ON THE BED OF THE LAKE . . .

. . . THE KRAKKEN'S *EGG!*

SUDDENLY, A DARK SHADOW APPEARS BEHIND THE CAPTAIN.

NOT HESITATING, CAPTAIN SHAW FIRES HIS HARPOON!

FWOOSH!

BUT THE SHADOW DODGES THE SPEAR.

THE SHADOW TURNS OUT TO BE BEN!

CAPTAIN SHAW
SHOWS BEN THE EGG
HE HAS FOUND.

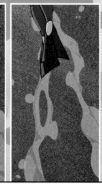

HE SWIMS BACK UP TO
THE SURFACE TO GET
HIS EQUIPMENT.

WHEN CAPTAIN SHAW SURFACES,
THERE IS A STRANGE BOAT
FLOATING NEXT TO HIS SHIP.

AS HE TRIES TO CLIMB UP THE LADDER TO HIS BOAT, SOMEBODY GRABS HIM BY THE ARM . . .

. . . AND THROWS HIM TO THE DECK!

DON'T YOU KNOW THAT NIGHT DIVING IS DANGEROUS, OLD TIMER? UNLESS, OF COURSE, YOU WENT WITH A FRIEND.

I WORK ALONE. I AIN'T GOT NO FRIENDS.

BEN EMERGES FROM UNDER THE WATER.

SPLASH!

I HAVEN'T GOT ANYTHING WORTH STEALING, EITHER!

YOU'VE GOT US ALL WRONG. ALL WE WANT IS SOME INFORMATION.

WHAT DID YOU SEE DOWN THERE?

NOTHING. SAME AS IT ALWAYS IS.

THWACK!

HE MASKED MAN STRIKES APTAIN SHAW WITH A HARD PUNCH AND KNOCKS HIM UNCONSCIOUS.

THE MASKED MAN IS JONAH, THE FOUNDER OF THE 'FRIENDS OF FISH' ORGANISATION!

HUH!

WELL, I HAVE TO BE SURE.

HUH?!

TAKE THE OLD MAN WITH US. FIND OUT IF HE KNOWS ANYTHING. WE'LL COME BACK LATER WITH A MINI-SUB TO GRAB THE REST OF THE EGGS.

JONAH DROPS A *LOCATION TRACKING DEVICE* INTO THE WATER.

BEEP!

BEEP!

SPLASH!

BEEP!

THEN HE ACTIVATES A *TIME BOMB*.

IN THE MEANTIME, I THINK HIS BOAT JUST GOT LOST AT SEA!

61

COME ON, FLY!
COME ON, BLAST OFF!

DIE, YOU
INSECT!

BOOM!

FWOOSH!

GLUG!

STINKFLY LAUNCHES
HIS SLIMY FLUID AT A
NEARBY TREE BRANCH.

HE USES THE SLIME TO PULL
HIMSELF UP ON TO THE TREE
TO ESCAPE THE GUNFIRE.

SLURRPP!

SWOOSH!

SPLASH!

LOOKS LIKE WE WERE BOTH A LITTLE TOO HARD-HEADED.
CRATES THEM UP?
OH, MAN! I BET THAT CRATE THE KRAKKEN TOOK FROM THE BOAT HAD HER EGGS IN IT!
WE'VE GOT TO STOP THEM! THEY SAID SOMETHING ABOUT GOING BACK TO A *CANNERY*.
ALL THIS TALK DOESN'T CHANGE A THING. A MOTHER OR NOT, THAT BEAST IS MINE.
LET'S GO. I HAVE A SPARE BOAT DOWN AT THE DOCKS.

FWOOSH!

JUST THEN, THE KRAKKEN BURSTS THROUGH THE SURFACE OF THE WATER.

THE KRAKKEN!

HUH?

GREAT! THE BIGGER THE KRAKKEN, THE BIGGER THE PAYDAY.

JONAH CLIMBS INTO HIS ROBOTIC DIVING SUIT.

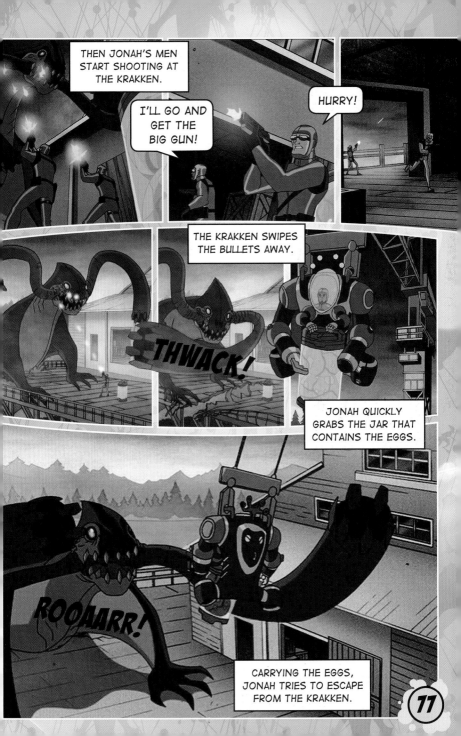

SUDDENLY, RIPJAWS BURSTS OUT OF THE WATER!

JONAH SHOOTS AT THE KRAKKEN TO DRIVE IT BACK INTO THE WATER.

YOU WANNA MESS WITH A MONSTER? TRY ME FOR SIZE!

GIVE BACK THE EGGS!

MEANWHILE, GRANDPA MAX AND GWEN ARE SNEAKING AROUND THE CANNERY, WHEN THEY HEAR A NOISE.

HMM . . .

HERE'S THE BIG GUN!

PSST!

OUT ON THE LAKE, ONE OF JONAH'S MEN HAS FALLEN OVERBOARD . . .

FREEZE!

. . . HE CLIMBS BACK INTO THE CANNERY AND FINDS GRANDPA MAX AND GWEN!

WHEN THE KRAKKEN SEES THE
BROKEN JAR, IT TURNS AND
RACES TOWARDS THE EGGS.

BUT JONAH ISN'T GOING TO
LET THE KRAKKEN TAKE THE
EGGS WITHOUT A FIGHT!

FWOOSH!

SWOOPING IN, JONAH
SEIZES THE EGGS.

ZAP!

JONAH RELEASES A SONAR ATTACK TO STOP THE KRAKKEN.

WHIZZ!

ZOOM!

AWW, TRYING TO SAVE YOUR BABIES. HOW SWEET . . . BUT STUPID!

FWOOSH!

YOU'VE GONE TOO FAR, JONAH!

RAAAA!

USING ALL OF HIS STRENGTH, RIPJAWS THROWS JONAH TO THE BOTTOM OF THE LAKE.

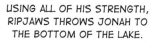

KA-BOOM!

JONAH ACTIVATES AN ELECTRIC CURRENT, GIVING RIPJAWS AN ELECTRIC SHOCK!

JONAH TRIES TO ESCAPE. RIPJAWS THROWS AN ANCHOR AT HIM.

THE ANCHOR HITS THE ROBOT SUIT AND THE ARM BREAKS IN HALF.

THE KRAKKEN BEGINS ANOTHER ATTACK.

THE KRAKKEN BREAKS THE CHAIN OFF THE ANCHOR.

SWOOSH!

THE EGGS SLIP OUT OF JONAH'S GRASP. RIPJAWS WASTES NO TIME AND GRABS THE PRECIOUS EGGS WITH HIS JAW!

ROOAARRR!

SEEING THAT RIPJAWS HAS THE EGGS, THE KRAKKEN FOLLOWS IN HOT PURSUIT!

RIPJAWS GENTLY PUTS THE KRAKKEN'S EGGS BACK INTO THE NEST.

THE KRAKKEN SURGES TOWARDS HER EGGS TO MAKE SURE THEY ARE SAFE.

REFUSING TO GIVE UP, JONAH BEGINS ANOTHER ATTACK ON THE KRAKKEN.

ROOAARRR!

THE KRAKKEN GRABS HOLD OF THE ROBOTIC DIVING SUIT AND CRUSHES IT.

CRASSHH!

. . . BUT IT DOESN'T QUITE GO AS HE PLANNED.

CLANK!

FURIOUS AT LOSING THE BATTLE, JONAH TAKES AIM WITH A SHARP BLADE . . .

ROOARRRRRR!

AS THE KRAKKEN OPENS ITS JAWS WIDE, RIPJAWS RACES FORWARD TO RESCUE JONAH.

RIPJAWS IS GOING TO DEAL WITH JONAH HIMSELF.

FWOOSH

BAM.

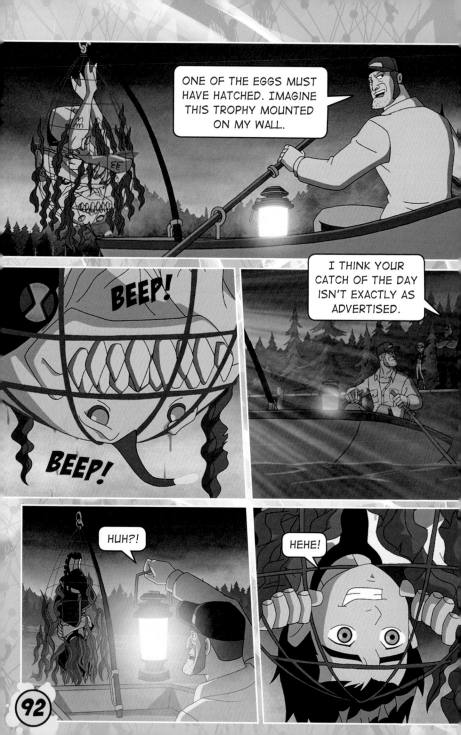

NAME: FOUR ARMS

ALIEN BACKGROUND:
FOUR ARMS DESCENDS
FROM THE PLANET
KHOROS. KHOROS IS
MADE UP OF DRY, HOT
DESERT LAND

SUPER POWER: HE IS ONE
OF THE STRONGEST ALIEN
FORMS. HE IS RARELY
DEFEATED IN A BATTLE THAT
REQUIRES PHYSICAL STRENGTH

PHYSICAL FACT: HE HAS FOUR
ARMS, FOUR EYES AND IS 10 FEET TALL! FOUR ARMS
IS CONSIDERED TO BE A GIANT COMPARED TO OTHER
LIFE FORMS

INTERESTING FACT: HE CAN LAUNCH AN AIR BLAST
ATTACK BY SLAMMING THE GROUND OR CLAPPING HIS
HANDS TOGETHER!

WEAKNESS: HIS MUSCLES GIVE HIM STRENGTH
BUT NOT SPEED. IT IS DIFFICULT FOR
FOUR ARMS TO DODGE ATTACKS OR FACE
QUICK ENEMIES

FOUR ARMS

BEN 10

EVER WISHED THE SCHOOL HOLIDAYS COULD BE MORE INTERESTING?

WIN A
£20 EGMONT
BOOK VOUCHER
EVERY MONTH!

WIN!

Simply go to
WWW.EGMONT.CO.UK/COMPETITION
and tell us which adventures
you would like to go on!